THE YEAR 2000 ENGAGEMENT CALENDAR

# ANSEL ADAMS

LITTLE, BROWN AND COMPANY    BOSTON · NEW YORK · LONDON

● New Moon

◐ First Quarter

○ Full Moon

◑ Last Quarter

FRONT COVER: Mount McKinley and Wonder Lake, Denali National Park, Alaska, 1947
BACK COVER: Ansel Adams, c. 1945, by Nancy Newhall

ISBN 0-8212-2576-6

Designed by Pentagram
Printed by Gardner Lithograph

Printed in the United States of America

# DECEMBER 1999/JANUARY 2000

**27** MONDAY

a.m.

p.m.

**28** TUESDAY

a.m.

p.m.

**29** WEDNESDAY

a.m.

p.m.

**30** THURSDAY

a.m.

p.m.

**31** FRIDAY

a.m.

p.m.

**1** SATURDAY

New Year's Day

**2** SUNDAY

# JANUARY

**3** MONDAY

a.m.

p.m.

**4** TUESDAY

a.m.

p.m.

**5** WEDNESDAY

a.m.

p.m.

**6** THURSDAY

a.m.

p.m.

**7** FRIDAY

a.m.

p.m.

**8** SATURDAY

**9** SUNDAY

**JANUARY**

| S | M | T | W | T | F | S |
|---|---|---|---|---|---|---|
|   |   |   |   |   |   | 1 |
| 2 | 3 | 4 | 5 | 6 | 7 | 8 |
| 9 | 10 | 11 | 12 | 13 | 14 | 15 |
| 16 | 17 | 18 | 19 | 20 | 21 | 22 |
| 23 | 24 | 25 | 26 | 27 | 28 | 29 |
| 30 | 31 |   |   |   |   |   |

**DECEMBER**

| S | M | T | W | T | F | S |
|---|---|---|---|---|---|---|
|   |   |   |   | 1 | 2 | 3 |
| 4 | 5 | 6 | 7 | 8 | 9 | 10 |
| 11 | 12 | 13 | 14 | 15 | 16 | 17 |
| 18 | 19 | 20 | 21 | 22 | 23 | 24 |
| 25 | 26 | 27 | 28 | 29 | 30 | 31 |

**FEBRUARY**

| S | M | T | W | T | F | S |
|---|---|---|---|---|---|---|
|   |   | 1 | 2 | 3 | 4 | 5 |
| 6 | 7 | 8 | 9 | 10 | 11 | 12 |
| 13 | 14 | 15 | 16 | 17 | 18 | 19 |
| 20 | 21 | 22 | 23 | 24 | 25 | 26 |
| 27 | 28 | 29 |   |   |   |   |

Pine Forest in Snow, Yosemite
National Park, California, c. 1932

Frozen Lake and Cliffs, Sequoia National Park, California, 1927

# JANUARY

| 10 MONDAY | 11 TUESDAY | 12 WEDNESDAY |
|---|---|---|
| a.m. | a.m. | a.m. *Snoed Day* |
| p.m. | p.m. | p.m. |

| 13 THURSDAY | 14 FRIDAY | 15 SATURDAY |
|---|---|---|
| a.m. | a.m. 6:30 Meet | WI |
| p.m. | p.m. | 16 SUNDAY |
| | | WI |

JANUARY
S M T W T F S
        1
2 3 4 5 6 7 8
9 10 11 12 13 14 15
16 17 18 19 20 21 22
23 24 25 26 27 28 29
30 31

DECEMBER
S M T W T F S
      1 2 3 4
5 6 7 8 9 10 11
12 13 14 15 16 17 18
19 20 21 22 23 24 25
26 27 28 29 30 31

FEBRUARY
S M T W T F S
    1 2 3 4 5
6 7 8 9 10 11 12
13 14 15 16 17 18 19
20 21 22 23 24 25 26
27 28 29

# JANUARY

**17** MONDAY

a.m.

p.m.

Martin Luther King Jr. Day

**18** TUESDAY

a.m.

p.m.

**19** WEDNESDAY

a.m.

*Sales Rally*

p.m.

**20** THURSDAY ○

a.m.

p.m.

**21** FRIDAY

a.m.

p.m.

**22** SATURDAY

**23** SUNDAY

**JANUARY**

| S | M | T | W | T | F | S |
|---|---|---|---|---|---|---|
|   |   |   |   |   |   | 1 |
| 2 | 3 | 4 | 5 | 6 | 7 | 8 |
| 9 | 10 | 11 | 12 | 13 | 14 | 15 |
| 16 | 17 | 18 | 19 | 20 | 21 | 22 |
| 23 | 24 | 25 | 26 | 27 | 28 | 29 |
| 30 | 31 |   |   |   |   |   |

**DECEMBER**

| S | M | T | W | T | F | S |
|---|---|---|---|---|---|---|
|   |   |   |   | 1 | 2 | 3 | 4 |
| 5 | 6 | 7 | 8 | 9 | 10 | 11 |
| 12 | 13 | 14 | 15 | 16 | 17 | 18 |
| 19 | 20 | 21 | 22 | 23 | 24 | 25 |
| 26 | 27 | 28 | 29 | 30 | 31 |   |

**FEBRUARY**

| S | M | T | W | T | F | S |
|---|---|---|---|---|---|---|
|   |   | 1 | 2 | 3 | 4 | 5 |
| 6 | 7 | 8 | 9 | 10 | 11 | 12 |
| 13 | 14 | 15 | 16 | 17 | 18 | 19 |
| 20 | 21 | 22 | 23 | 24 | 25 | 26 |
| 27 | 28 | 29 |   |   |   |   |

Mount McKinley from Stoney
Pass, Denali National Park,
Alaska, 1948

Young Oaks in Snow, Yosemite National Park, California, c. 1938

# JANUARY

**24** MONDAY

a.m.

p.m.

**25** TUESDAY

a.m.

p.m.

**26** WEDNESDAY

a.m.

p.m.

**27** THURSDAY

a.m.

p.m.

**28** FRIDAY ◑

a.m.

p.m.

**29** SATURDAY

**30** SUNDAY

# JANUARY/FEBRUARY

**31 MONDAY**

a.m. ISITV

p.m.

**1 TUESDAY**

a.m. ISITV

Tally Sheets Due

p.m.

**2 WEDNESDAY**

a.m. ISITV

p.m.

**3 THURSDAY**

a.m.

p.m.

**4 FRIDAY**

a.m.

p.m.

**5 SATURDAY**

**6 SUNDAY**

**FEBRUARY**

| S | M | T | W | T | F | S |
|---|---|---|---|---|---|---|
|   |   | 1 | 2 | 3 | 4 | 5 |
| 6 | 7 | 8 | 9 | 10 | 11 | 12 |
| 13 | 14 | 15 | 16 | 17 | 18 | 19 |
| 20 | 21 | 22 | 23 | 24 | 25 | 26 |
| 27 | 28 | 29 |   |   |   |   |

**JANUARY**

| S | M | T | W | T | F | S |
|---|---|---|---|---|---|---|
|   |   |   |   |   |   | 1 |
| 2 | 3 | 4 | 5 | 6 | 7 | 8 |
| 9 | 10 | 11 | 12 | 13 | 14 | 15 |
| 16 | 17 | 18 | 19 | 20 | 21 | 22 |
| 23 | 24 | 25 | 26 | 27 | 28 | 29 |
| 30 | 31 |   |   |   |   |   |

**MARCH**

| S | M | T | W | T | F | S |
|---|---|---|---|---|---|---|
|   |   | 1 | 2 | 3 | 4 |   |
| 5 | 6 | 7 | 8 | 9 | 10 | 11 |
| 12 | 13 | 14 | 15 | 16 | 17 | 18 |
| 19 | 20 | 21 | 22 | 23 | 24 | 25 |
| 26 | 27 | 28 | 29 | 30 | 31 |   |

Mount Robson, Jasper National Park, Canada, 1928

Ski Tips in Snow, Yosemite National Park,
California, c. 1930

# FEBRUARY

**7** MONDAY

a.m.

p.m.

**8** TUESDAY

a.m.

p.m.

**9** WEDNESDAY

a.m.

p.m.

**10** THURSDAY

a.m.

*Company Meeting*

p.m.

**11** FRIDAY

a.m.

p.m.

**12** SATURDAY

Lincoln's Birthday

**13** SUNDAY

# FEBRUARY

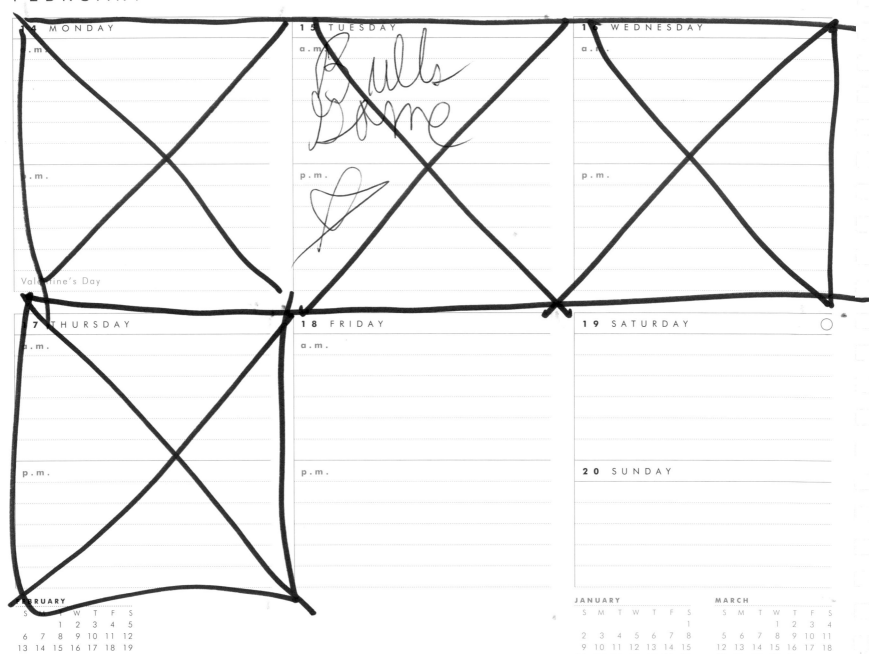

**14 MONDAY**

a.m.

p.m.

Valentine's Day

**15 TUESDAY**

a.m.

Bulls
Game

p.m.

**16 WEDNESDAY**

a.m.

p.m.

**17 THURSDAY**

a.m.

p.m.

**18 FRIDAY**

a.m.

p.m.

**19 SATURDAY**

**20 SUNDAY**

**FEBRUARY**

| S | M | T | W | T | F | S |
|---|---|---|---|---|---|---|
| | | 1 | 2 | 3 | 4 | 5 |
| 6 | 7 | 8 | 9 | 10 | 11 | 12 |
| 13 | 14 | 15 | 16 | 17 | 18 | 19 |
| 20 | 21 | 22 | 23 | 24 | 25 | 26 |
| 27 | 28 | 29 | | | | |

**JANUARY**

| S | M | T | W | T | F | S |
|---|---|---|---|---|---|---|
| | | | | | | 1 |
| 2 | 3 | 4 | 5 | 6 | 7 | 8 |
| 9 | 10 | 11 | 12 | 13 | 14 | 15 |
| 16 | 17 | 18 | 19 | 20 | 21 | 22 |
| 23 | 24 | 25 | 26 | 27 | 28 | 29 |
| 30 | 31 | | | | | |

**MARCH**

| S | M | T | W | T | F | S |
|---|---|---|---|---|---|---|
| | | 1 | 2 | 3 | 4 |
| 5 | 6 | 7 | 8 | 9 | 10 | 11 |
| 12 | 13 | 14 | 15 | 16 | 17 | 18 |
| 19 | 20 | 21 | 22 | 23 | 24 | 25 |
| 26 | 27 | 28 | 29 | 30 | 31 | |

Trees and Fence in Snow, Yosemite National Park, California, c. 1936

Evening Cloud, Ellery Lake, Sierra Nevada, California, 1934

# FEBRUARY

**21** MONDAY

a.m.

p.m.

Presidents' Day

**22** TUESDAY

a.m.

p.m.

Washington's Birthday

**23** WEDNESDAY

a.m. Sunbeam

p.m.

**24** THURSDAY

a.m. Martex

p.m.

**25** FRIDAY

a.m. NVE

p.m.

**26** SATURDAY

**27** SUNDAY

**FEBRUARY**

| S | M | T | W | T | F | S |
|---|---|---|---|---|---|---|
|   |   | 1 | 2 | 3 | 4 | 5 |
| 6 | 7 | 8 | 9 | 10 | 11 | 12 |
| 13 | 14 | 15 | 16 | 17 | 18 | 19 |
| 20 | 21 | 22 | 23 | 24 | 25 | 26 |
| 27 | 28 | 29 |   |   |   |   |

**JANUARY**

| S | M | T | W | T | F | S |
|---|---|---|---|---|---|---|
|   |   |   |   |   |   | 1 |
| 2 | 3 | 4 | 5 | 6 | 7 | 8 |
| 9 | 10 | 11 | 12 | 13 | 14 | 15 |
| 16 | 17 | 18 | 19 | 20 | 21 | 22 |
| 23 | 24 | 25 | 26 | 27 | 28 | 29 |
| 30 | 31 |   |   |   |   |   |

**MARCH**

| S | M | T | W | T | F | S |
|---|---|---|---|---|---|---|
|   |   | 1 | 2 | 3 | 4 |   |
| 5 | 6 | 7 | 8 | 9 | 10 | 11 |
| 12 | 13 | 14 | 15 | 16 | 17 | 18 |
| 19 | 20 | 21 | 22 | 23 | 24 | 25 |
| 26 | 27 | 28 | 29 | 30 | 31 |   |

**28** MONDAY
a.m.

p.m.

**29** TUESDAY
a.m.

p.m.

**1** WEDNESDAY
a.m.

p.m.

**2** THURSDAY
a.m.

p.m.

**3** FRIDAY
a.m.

p.m.

**4** SATURDAY

**5** SUNDAY

*Trading Times, Message Renewal*

**MARCH**

| S | M | T | W | T | F | S |
|---|---|---|---|---|---|---|
|   |   |   | 1 | 2 | 3 | 4 |
| 5 | 6 | 7 | 8 | 9 | 10 | 11 |
| 12 | 13 | 14 | 15 | 16 | 17 | 18 |
| 19 | 20 | 21 | 22 | 23 | 24 | 25 |
| 26 | 27 | 28 | 29 | 30 | 31 |   |

**FEBRUARY**

| S | M | T | W | T | F | S |
|---|---|---|---|---|---|---|
|   |   | 1 | 2 | 3 | 4 | 5 |
| 6 | 7 | 8 | 9 | 10 | 11 | 12 |
| 13 | 14 | 15 | 16 | 17 | 18 | 19 |
| 20 | 21 | 22 | 23 | 24 | 25 | 26 |
| 27 | 28 | 29 |   |   |   |   |

**APRIL**

| S | M | T | W | T | F | S |
|---|---|---|---|---|---|---|
|   |   |   |   |   |   | 1 |
| 2 | 3 | 4 | 5 | 6 | 7 | 8 |
| 9 | 10 | 11 | 12 | 13 | 14 | 15 |
| 16 | 17 | 18 | 19 | 20 | 21 | 22 |
| 23 | 24 | 25 | 26 | 27 | 28 | 29 |
| 30 |   |   |   |   |   |   |

Clearing Storm, Sonoma County H

**7** TUESDAY

a.m.

p.m.

**8** WEDNESDAY

a.m.

p.m.

Ash Wednesday

**10** FRIDAY

a.m.

p.m.

**11** SATURDAY

**12** SUNDAY

# MARCH

## 13 MONDAY ◑
a.m.

p.m.

## 14 TUESDAY
a.m.

p.m.

## 15 WEDNESDAY
a.m.

*call gut*
*Trader 630 620 355*

p.m.

## 16 THURSDAY
a.m.

p.m.

## 17 FRIDAY
a.m.

*leave →*
*CO*

p.m.

St. Patrick's Day

## 18 SATURDAY

*Widespread*
*Tix 4 Sale*

## 19 SUNDAY ○

**MARCH**

| S | M | T | W | T | F | S |
|---|---|---|---|---|---|---|
|   |   |   | 1 | 2 | 3 | 4 |
| 5 | 6 | 7 | 8 | 9 | 10 | 11 |
| 12 | 13 | 14 | 15 | 16 | 17 | 18 |
| 19 | 20 | 21 | 22 | 23 | 24 | 25 |
| 26 | 27 | 28 | 29 | 30 | 31 |   |

**FEBRUARY**

| S | M | T | W | T | F | S |
|---|---|---|---|---|---|---|
|   |   |   | 1 | 2 | 3 | 4 | 5 |
| 6 | 7 | 8 | 9 | 10 | 11 | 12 |
| 13 | 14 | 15 | 16 | 17 | 18 | 19 |
| 20 | 21 | 22 | 23 | 24 | 25 | 26 |
| 27 | 28 | 29 |   |   |   |   |

**APRIL**

| S | M | T | W | T | F | S |
|---|---|---|---|---|---|---|
|   |   |   |   |   |   | 1 |
| 2 | 3 | 4 | 5 | 6 | 7 | 8 |
| 9 | 10 | 11 | 12 | 13 | 14 | 15 |
| 16 | 17 | 18 | 19 | 20 | 21 | 22 |
| 23 | 24 | 25 | 26 | 27 | 28 | 29 |
| 30 |   |   |   |   |   |   |

Grass in Rain, Glacier Bay National Park, Alaska, 1948

Oak Tree, Rain, Sonoma County, California, c. 1960

# MARCH

**20** MONDAY

a.m. *CO*

p.m. *CO*

Vernal Equinox

**21** TUESDAY

a.m. *CO*

p.m. *CO*

**22** WEDNESDAY

a.m. *CO*

p.m. *CO*

**23** THURSDAY

a.m. *CO*

p.m. *C C*

**24** FRIDAY

a.m. *CO*

p.m. *CO*

**25** SATURDAY

*CO*

**26** SUNDAY

*Bach franco*

**MARCH**

| S | M | T | W | T | F | S |
|---|---|---|---|---|---|---|
|   |   |   | 1 | 2 | 3 | 4 |
| 5 | 6 | 7 | 8 | 9 | 10 | 11 |
| 12 | 13 | 14 | 15 | 16 | 17 | 18 |
| 19 | 20 | 21 | 22 | 23 | 24 | 25 |
| 26 | 27 | 28 | 29 | 30 | 31 |   |

**FEBRUARY**

| S | M | T | W | T | F | S |
|---|---|---|---|---|---|---|
|   |   | 1 | 2 | 3 | 4 | 5 |
| 6 | 7 | 8 | 9 | 10 | 11 | 12 |
| 13 | 14 | 15 | 16 | 17 | 18 | 19 |
| 20 | 21 | 22 | 23 | 24 | 25 | 26 |
| 27 | 28 | 29 |   |   |   |   |

**APRIL**

| S | M | T | W | T | F | S |
|---|---|---|---|---|---|---|
|   |   |   |   |   |   | 1 |
| 2 | 3 | 4 | 5 | 6 | 7 | 8 |
| 9 | 10 | 11 | 12 | 13 | 14 | 15 |
| 16 | 17 | 18 | 19 | 20 | 21 | 22 |
| 23 | 24 | 25 | 26 | 27 | 28 | 29 |
| 30 |   |   |   |   |   |   |

# MARCH/APRIL

**27** MONDAY ◑

a.m.

p.m.

**28** TUESDAY

a.m.

p.m.

**29** WEDNESDAY

a.m.

p.m.

**30** THURSDAY

a.m.

p.m.

**31** FRIDAY

a.m.

p.m.

**1** SATURDAY

**2** SUNDAY

Daylight Saving Time begins

**MARCH**

| S | M | T | W | T | F | S |
|---|---|---|---|---|---|---|
| | | | 1 | 2 | 3 | 4 |
| 5 | 6 | 7 | 8 | 9 | 10 | 11 |
| 12 | 13 | 14 | 15 | 16 | 17 | 18 |
| 19 | 20 | 21 | 22 | 23 | 24 | 25 |
| 26 | 27 | 28 | 29 | 30 | 31 | |

**FEBRUARY**

| S | M | T | W | T | F | S |
|---|---|---|---|---|---|---|
| | | | 1 | 2 | 3 | 4 |
| 6 | 7 | 8 | 9 | 10 | 11 | 12 |
| 13 | 14 | 15 | 16 | 17 | 18 | 19 |
| 20 | 21 | 22 | 23 | 24 | 25 | 26 |
| 27 | 28 | 29 | | | | |

**APRIL**

| S | M | T | W | T | F | S |
|---|---|---|---|---|---|---|
| | | | | | | 1 |
| 2 | 3 | 4 | 5 | 6 | 7 | 8 |
| 9 | 10 | 11 | 12 | 13 | 14 | 15 |
| 16 | 17 | 18 | 19 | 20 | 21 | 22 |
| 23 | 24 | 25 | 26 | 27 | 28 | 29 |
| 30 | | | | | | |

Cypress and Fog, Pebble Beach, California, 1965

Vine and Rocks, Island of Hawaii, 1948

# APRIL

## 3 MONDAY
a.m.

p.m.

## 4 TUESDAY
a.m.

p.m.

## 5 WEDNESDAY
a.m.

*Trading Time*

*630·680-3855*

p.m.

## 6 THURSDAY
a.m.

p.m.

## 7 FRIDAY
a.m.

p.m.

## 8 SATURDAY

## 9 SUNDAY

**APRIL**

| S | M | T | W | T | F | S |
|---|---|---|---|---|---|---|
|   |   |   |   |   |   | 1 |
| 2 | 3 | 4 | 5 | 6 | 7 | 8 |
| 9 | 10 | 11 | 12 | 13 | 14 | 15 |
| 16 | 17 | 18 | 19 | 20 | 21 | 22 |
| 23 | 24 | 25 | 26 | 27 | 28 | 29 |
| 30 |   |   |   |   |   |   |

**MARCH**

| S | M | T | W | T | F | S |
|---|---|---|---|---|---|---|
|   |   |   | 1 | 2 | 3 | 4 |
| 5 | 6 | 7 | 8 | 9 | 10 | 11 |
| 12 | 13 | 14 | 15 | 16 | 17 | 18 |
| 19 | 20 | 21 | 22 | 23 | 24 | 25 |
| 26 | 27 | 28 | 29 | 30 | 31 |   |

**MAY**

| S | M | T | W | T | F | S |
|---|---|---|---|---|---|---|
|   | 1 | 2 | 3 | 4 | 5 | 6 |
| 7 | 8 | 9 | 10 | 11 | 12 | 13 |
| 14 | 15 | 16 | 17 | 18 | 19 | 20 |
| 21 | 22 | 23 | 24 | 25 | 26 | 27 |
| 28 | 29 | 30 | 31 |   |   |   |

# APRIL

**10** MONDAY

a.m.

p.m.

**11** TUESDAY

a.m.

p.m.

**12** WEDNESDAY

a.m.

p.m.

**13** THURSDAY

a.m.

p.m.

**14** FRIDAY

a.m.

p.m.

**15** SATURDAY

Go to Florida

**16** SUNDAY

Palm Sunday

Road After Rain, North Coast, Northern California, 1959

Early Morning, Merced River, Yosemite National Park, California, c. 1950

# APRIL

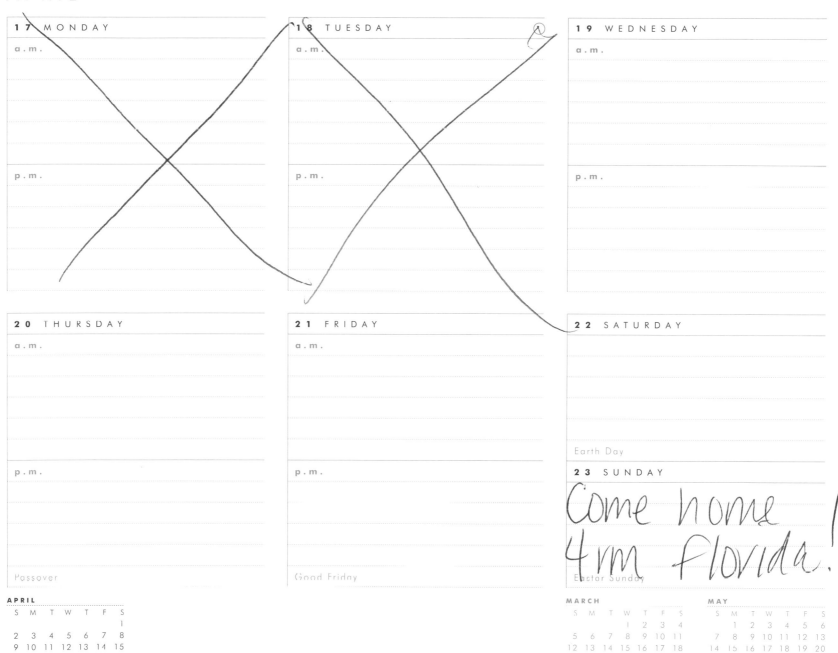

**17** MONDAY

a.m.

p.m.

**18** TUESDAY

a.m.

p.m.

**19** WEDNESDAY

a.m.

p.m.

**20** THURSDAY

a.m.

p.m.

Passover

**21** FRIDAY

a.m.

p.m.

Good Friday

**22** SATURDAY

Earth Day

**23** SUNDAY

Easter Sunday

Come home!
4rm Florida!

**APRIL**

S M T W T F S
              1
2 3 4 5 6 7 8
9 10 11 12 13 14 15
16 17 18 19 20 21 22
23 24 25 26 27 28 29
30

**MARCH**

S M T W T F S
      1 2 3 4
5 6 7 8 9 10 11
12 13 14 15 16 17 18
19 20 21 22 23 24 25
26 27 28 29 30 31

**MAY**

S M T W T F S
  1 2 3 4 5 6
7 8 9 10 11 12 13
14 15 16 17 18 19 20
21 22 23 24 25 26 27
28 29 30 31

# APRIL

## 24 MONDAY
a.m.

p.m.

## 25 TUESDAY
a.m.

*Reading Times Renew*
*630-520-7355*

p.m.

*10:00 training*
*FT James*

## 26 WEDNESDAY ◐
a.m.

p.m.

## 27 THURSDAY
a.m.

p.m.

## 28 FRIDAY
a.m.

*6:00*

p.m.

## 29 SATURDAY

## 30 SUNDAY

*Cubs Game*

**APRIL**

| S | M | T | W | T | F | S |
|---|---|---|---|---|---|---|
|   |   |   |   |   |   | 1 |
| 2 | 3 | 4 | 5 | 6 | 7 | 8 |
| 9 | 10 | 11 | 12 | 13 | 14 | 15 |
| 16 | 17 | 18 | 19 | 20 | 21 | 22 |
| 23 | 24 | 25 | 26 | 27 | 28 | 29 |
| 30 |   |   |   |   |   |   |

**MARCH**

| S | M | T | W | T | F | S |
|---|---|---|---|---|---|---|
|   |   |   | 1 | 2 | 3 | 4 |
| 5 | 6 | 7 | 8 | 9 | 10 | 11 |
| 12 | 13 | 14 | 15 | 16 | 17 | 18 |
| 19 | 20 | 21 | 22 | 23 | 24 | 25 |
| 26 | 27 | 28 | 29 | 30 | 31 |   |

**MAY**

| S | M | T | W | T | F | S |
|---|---|---|---|---|---|---|
|   | 1 | 2 | 3 | 4 | 5 | 6 |
| 7 | 8 | 9 | 10 | 11 | 12 | 13 |
| 14 | 15 | 16 | 17 | 18 | 19 | 20 |
| 21 | 22 | 23 | 24 | 25 | 26 | 27 |
| 28 | 29 | 30 | 31 |   |   |   |

Pywiack Cascade, Tenaya
Canyon, Yosemite National Park,
California, c. 1935

Royal Arches from Glacier Point, Yosemite National Park, California, c. 1940

# MAY

**1** MONDAY

a.m.

p.m.

**2** TUESDAY

a.m.

p.m.

**3** WEDNESDAY

a.m. *Relax*

*Records*

p.m.

**4** THURSDAY

a.m.

*Dentist*

p.m.

**5** FRIDAY

a.m.

*Mon*

p.m.

**6** SATURDAY

*W I ?*

**7** SUNDAY

# MAY

## 8 MONDAY
a.m.

730 pm
Dr Cook Dentist

p.m.

## 9 TUESDAY
a.m.

p.m.

## 10 WEDNESDAY
a.m.

Trading Time
630-620-7355

p.m.

## 11 THURSDAY
a.m.

p.m.

## 12 FRIDAY
a.m.

p.m.

## 13 SATURDAY

## 14 SUNDAY

Mother's Day

**MAY**

| S | M | T | W | T | F | S |
|---|---|---|---|---|---|---|
|   | 1 | 2 | 3 | 4 | 5 | 6 |
| 7 | 8 | 9 | 10 | 11 | 12 | 13 |
| 14 | 15 | 16 | 17 | 18 | 19 | 20 |
| 21 | 22 | 23 | 24 | 25 | 26 | 27 |
| 28 | 29 | 30 | 31 |   |   |   |

**APRIL**

| S | M | T | W | T | F | S |
|---|---|---|---|---|---|---|
|   |   |   |   |   |   | 1 |
| 2 | 3 | 4 | 5 | 6 | 7 | 8 |
| 9 | 10 | 11 | 12 | 13 | 14 | 15 |
| 16 | 17 | 18 | 19 | 20 | 21 | 22 |
| 23 | 24 | 25 | 26 | 27 | 28 | 29 |
| 30 |   |   |   |   |   |   |

**JUNE**

| S | M | T | W | T | F | S |
|---|---|---|---|---|---|---|
|   |   |   |   | 1 | 2 | 3 |
| 4 | 5 | 6 | 7 | 8 | 9 | 10 |
| 11 | 12 | 13 | 14 | 15 | 16 | 17 |
| 18 | 19 | 20 | 21 | 22 | 23 | 24 |
| 25 | 26 | 27 | 28 | 29 | 30 |   |

Bridal Veil Fall, Yosomite National
Park, California, 1927

Tenaya Creek, Dogwood, Rain, Yosemite National Park, California, 1950

# MAY

**15** MONDAY

a.m. *Dentist*

*7.30*

p.m.

**16** TUESDAY

a.m.

p.m.

**17** WEDNESDAY

a.m.

p.m.

**18** THURSDAY ○

a.m.

p.m.

**19** FRIDAY

a.m.

p.m.

**20** SATURDAY

a.m.

**21** SUNDAY

**MAY**

| S | M | T | W | T | F | S |
|---|---|---|---|---|---|---|
|   | 1 | 2 | 3 | 4 | 5 | 6 |
| 7 | 8 | 9 | 10 | 11 | 12 | 13 |
| 14 | 15 | 16 | 17 | 18 | 19 | 20 |
| 21 | 22 | 23 | 24 | 25 | 26 | 27 |
| 28 | 29 | 30 | 31 |   |   |   |

**APRIL**

| S | M | T | W | T | F | S |
|---|---|---|---|---|---|---|
|   |   |   |   |   |   | 1 |
| 2 | 3 | 4 | 5 | 6 | 7 | 8 |
| 9 | 10 | 11 | 12 | 13 | 14 | 15 |
| 16 | 17 | 18 | 19 | 20 | 21 | 22 |
| 23 | 24 | 25 | 26 | 27 | 28 | 29 |
| 30 |   |   |   |   |   |   |

**JUNE**

| S | M | T | W | T | F | S |
|---|---|---|---|---|---|---|
|   |   |   |   | 1 | 2 | 3 |
| 4 | 5 | 6 | 7 | 8 | 9 | 10 |
| 11 | 12 | 13 | 14 | 15 | 16 | 17 |
| 18 | 19 | 20 | 21 | 22 | 23 | 24 |
| 25 | 26 | 27 | 28 | 29 | 30 |   |

# MAY

**22** MONDAY

a.m.

p.m.

Victoria Day (Canada)

**23** TUESDAY

a.m.

p.m.

**24** WEDNESDAY

a.m.

p.m.

**25** THURSDAY

a.m.

p.m.

**26** FRIDAY

a.m.

p.m.

**27** SATURDAY

Phish TIX
4 alpine (414-276-4545

**28** SUNDAY

**MAY**
S M T W T F S
          1  2  3  4  5  6
7  8  9  10 11 12 13
14 15 16 17 18 19 20
21 22 23 24 25 26 27
28 29 30 31

**APRIL**
S M T W T F S
                  1
2  3  4  5  6  7  8
9  10 11 12 13 14 15
16 17 18 19 20 21 22
23 24 25 26 27 28 29
30

**JUNE**
S M T W T F S
            1  2  3
4  5  6  7  8  9  10
11 12 13 14 15 16 17
18 19 20 21 22 23 24
25 26 27 28 29 30

El Capitan, Yosemite National Park,
California, 1952

Upper Yosemite Falls and Apple Blossoms, Yosemite National Park, California, 1945

# MAY/JUNE

## 29 MONDAY

a.m.

p.m.

Memorial Day Observed

## 30 TUESDAY

a.m.

Shawn
B.Day

p.m.

Memorial Day

## 31 WEDNESDAY

a.m.

Trading Tems
630-620-7355

p.m.

Laura
BorB

Shipt Tu
for Search

## 1 THURSDAY

a.m.

p.m.

## 2 FRIDAY

a.m.

p.m.

## 3 SATURDAY

## 4 SUNDAY

**MAY**

| S | M | T | W | T | F | S |
|---|---|---|---|---|---|---|
|   | 1 | 2 | 3 | 4 | 5 | 6 |
| 7 | 8 | 9 | 10 | 11 | 12 | 13 |
| 14 | 15 | 16 | 17 | 18 | 19 | 20 |
| 21 | 22 | 23 | 24 | 25 | 26 | 27 |
| 28 | 29 | 30 | 31 |   |   |   |

**APRIL**

| S | M | T | W | T | F | S |
|---|---|---|---|---|---|---|
|   |   |   |   |   |   | 1 |
| 2 | 3 | 4 | 5 | 6 | 7 | 8 |
| 9 | 10 | 11 | 12 | 13 | 14 | 15 |
| 16 | 17 | 18 | 19 | 20 | 21 | 22 |
| 23 | 24 | 25 | 26 | 27 | 28 | 29 |
| 30 |   |   |   |   |   |   |

**JUNE**

| S | M | T | W | T | F | S |
|---|---|---|---|---|---|---|
|   |   |   |   | 1 | 2 | 3 |
| 4 | 5 | 6 | 7 | 8 | 9 | 10 |
| 11 | 12 | 13 | 14 | 15 | 16 | 17 |
| 18 | 19 | 20 | 21 | 22 | 23 | 24 |
| 25 | 26 | 27 | 28 | 29 | 30 |   |

# JUNE

**5** MONDAY

a.m.

p.m.

**6** TUESDAY

a.m.

p.m.

**7** WEDNESDAY

a.m.

p.m.

**8** THURSDAY

a.m.

p.m.

**9** FRIDAY

a.m.

p.m.

**10** SATURDAY

**11** SUNDAY

Nevada Fall, Rainbow, Yosemite National
Park, California, 1946

Half Dome and Clouds, Yosemite National Park, California, c. 1940

# JUNE

## 12 MONDAY
a.m.

p.m.

## 13 TUESDAY
a.m.

*Columbo*

p.m.

## 14 WEDNESDAY
a.m.

p.m.

Flag Day

## 15 THURSDAY
a.m.

*B-Day*

p.m.

## 16 FRIDAY
a.m.

p.m.

## 17 SATURDAY

## 18 SUNDAY

Father's Day

**JUNE**

| S | M | T | W | T | F | S |
|---|---|---|---|---|---|---|
|   |   |   |   | 1 | 2 | 3 |
| 4 | 5 | 6 | 7 | 8 | 9 | 10 |
| 11 | 12 | 13 | 14 | 15 | 16 | 17 |
| 18 | 19 | 20 | 21 | 22 | 23 | 24 |
| 25 | 26 | 27 | 28 | 29 | 30 |   |

**MAY**

| S | M | T | W | T | F | S |
|---|---|---|---|---|---|---|
|   | 1 | 2 | 3 | 4 | 5 | 6 |
| 7 | 8 | 9 | 10 | 11 | 12 | 13 |
| 14 | 15 | 16 | 17 | 18 | 19 | 20 |
| 21 | 22 | 23 | 24 | 25 | 26 | 27 |
| 28 | 29 | 30 | 31 |   |   |   |

**JULY**

| S | M | T | W | T | F | S |
|---|---|---|---|---|---|---|
|   |   |   |   |   |   | 1 |
| 2 | 3 | 4 | 5 | 6 | 7 | 8 |
| 9 | 10 | 11 | 12 | 13 | 14 | 15 |
| 16 | 17 | 18 | 19 | 20 | 21 | 22 |
| 23 | 24 | 25 | 26 | 27 | 28 | 29 |
| 30 | 31 |   |   |   |   |   |

# JUNE

**19** MONDAY

a.m.

p.m.

**20** TUESDAY

a.m.

p.m.

Summer Solstice

**21** WEDNESDAY

a.m.

p.m.

**22** THURSDAY

a.m.

p.m.

**23** FRIDAY

a.m.

p.m.

**24** SATURDAY

**25** SUNDAY

**JUNE**

| S | M | T | W | T | F | S |
|---|---|---|---|---|---|---|
| | | | | 1 | 2 | 3 |
| 4 | 5 | 6 | 7 | 8 | 9 | 10 |
| 11 | 12 | 13 | 14 | 15 | 16 | 17 |
| 18 | 19 | 20 | 21 | 22 | 23 | 24 |
| 25 | 26 | 27 | 28 | 29 | 30 | |

**MAY**

| S | M | T | W | T | F | S |
|---|---|---|---|---|---|---|
| | 1 | 2 | 3 | 4 | 5 | 6 |
| 7 | 8 | 9 | 10 | 11 | 12 | 13 |
| 14 | 15 | 16 | 17 | 18 | 19 | 20 |
| 21 | 22 | 23 | 24 | 25 | 26 | 27 |
| 28 | 29 | 30 | 31 | | | |

**JULY**

| S | M | T | W | T | F | S |
|---|---|---|---|---|---|---|
| | | | | | | 1 |
| 2 | 3 | 4 | 5 | 6 | 7 | 8 |
| 9 | 10 | 11 | 12 | 13 | 14 | 15 |
| 16 | 17 | 18 | 19 | 20 | 21 | 22 |
| 23 | 24 | 25 | 26 | 27 | 28 | 29 |
| 30 | 31 | | | | | |

# JUNE / JULY

## 26 MONDAY
a.m.

p.m.

## 27 TUESDAY
a.m.

p.m.

## 28 WEDNESDAY
a.m.

p.m.

## 29 THURSDAY
a.m.

p.m.

## 30 FRIDAY
a.m.

p.m.

## 1 SATURDAY

Canada Day (Canada)

## 2 SUNDAY

### JUNE
| S | M | T | W | T | F | S |
|---|---|---|---|---|---|---|
|   |   |   |   | 1 | 2 | 3 |
| 4 | 5 | 6 | 7 | 8 | 9 | 10 |
| 11 | 12 | 13 | 14 | 15 | 16 | 17 |
| 18 | 19 | 20 | 21 | 22 | 23 | 24 |
| 25 | 26 | 27 | 28 | 29 | 30 |   |

### MAY
| S | M | T | W | T | F | S |
|---|---|---|---|---|---|---|
|   | 1 | 2 | 3 | 4 | 5 | 6 |
| 7 | 8 | 9 | 10 | 11 | 12 | 13 |
| 14 | 15 | 16 | 17 | 18 | 19 | 20 |
| 21 | 22 | 23 | 24 | 25 | 26 | 27 |
| 28 | 29 | 30 | 31 |   |   |   |

### JULY
| S | M | T | W | T | F | S |
|---|---|---|---|---|---|---|
|   |   |   |   |   |   | 1 |
| 2 | 3 | 4 | 5 | 6 | 7 | 8 |
| 9 | 10 | 11 | 12 | 13 | 14 | 15 |
| 16 | 17 | 18 | 19 | 20 | 21 | 22 |
| 23 | 24 | 25 | 26 | 27 | 28 | 29 |
| 30 | 31 |   |   |   |   |   |

# JULY

**3** MONDAY

a.m.

p.m.

**4** TUESDAY

a.m.

p.m.

Independence Day

**5** WEDNESDAY

a.m.

p.m.

**6** THURSDAY

a.m.

p.m.

**7** FRIDAY

a.m.

p.m.

**8** SATURDAY ◗

**9** SUNDAY

**JULY**

| S | M | T | W | T | F | S |
|---|---|---|---|---|---|---|
|   |   |   |   |   |   | 1 |
| 2 | 3 | 4 | 5 | 6 | 7 | 8 |
| 9 | 10 | 11 | 12 | 13 | 14 | 15 |
| 16 | 17 | 18 | 19 | 20 | 21 | 22 |
| 23 | 24 | 25 | 26 | 27 | 28 | 29 |
| 30 | 31 |   |   |   |   |   |

**JUNE**

| S | M | T | W | T | F | S |
|---|---|---|---|---|---|---|
|   |   |   |   | 1 | 2 | 3 |
| 4 | 5 | 6 | 7 | 8 | 9 | 10 |
| 11 | 12 | 13 | 14 | 15 | 16 | 17 |
| 18 | 19 | 20 | 21 | 22 | 23 | 24 |
| 25 | 26 | 27 | 28 | 29 | 30 |   |

**AUGUST**

| S | M | T | W | T | F | S |
|---|---|---|---|---|---|---|
|   |   | 1 | 2 | 3 | 4 | 5 |
| 6 | 7 | 8 | 9 | 10 | 11 | 12 |
| 13 | 14 | 15 | 16 | 17 | 18 | 19 |
| 20 | 21 | 22 | 23 | 24 | 25 | 26 |
| 27 | 28 | 29 | 30 | 31 |   |   |

Clouds, View Down Tyndall Creek, Sequoia National Park, California, c. 1932

Mount Wynne, Kings Canyon National Park, California, c. 1932

# JULY

**10** MONDAY

a.m.

p.m.

**11** TUESDAY

a.m.

p.m.

**12** WEDNESDAY

a.m.

p.m.

**13** THURSDAY

a.m.

p.m.

**14** FRIDAY

a.m.

p.m.

**15** SATURDAY

**16** SUNDAY

**JULY**

| S | M | T | W | T | F | S |
|---|---|---|---|---|---|---|
|   |   |   |   |   |   | 1 |
| 2 | 3 | 4 | 5 | 6 | 7 | 8 |
| 9 | 10 | 11 | 12 | 13 | 14 | 15 |
| 16 | 17 | 18 | 19 | 20 | 21 | 22 |
| 23 | 24 | 25 | 26 | 27 | 28 | 29 |
| 30 | 31 |   |   |   |   |   |

**JUNE**

| S | M | T | W | T | F | S |
|---|---|---|---|---|---|---|
|   |   |   |   | 1 | 2 | 3 |
| 4 | 5 | 6 | 7 | 8 | 9 | 10 |
| 11 | 12 | 13 | 14 | 15 | 16 | 17 |
| 18 | 19 | 20 | 21 | 22 | 23 | 24 |
| 25 | 26 | 27 | 28 | 29 | 30 |   |

**AUGUST**

| S | M | T | W | T | F | S |
|---|---|---|---|---|---|---|
|   |   | 1 | 2 | 3 | 4 | 5 |
| 6 | 7 | 8 | 9 | 10 | 11 | 12 |
| 13 | 14 | 15 | 16 | 17 | 18 | 19 |
| 20 | 21 | 22 | 23 | 24 | 25 | 26 |
| 27 | 28 | 29 | 30 | 31 |   |   |

# JULY

**17** MONDAY

a.m.

p.m.

**18** TUESDAY

a.m.

p.m.

**19** WEDNESDAY

a.m.

p.m.

**20** THURSDAY

a.m.

p.m.

**21** FRIDAY

a.m.

p.m.

**22** SATURDAY

**23** SUNDAY

**JULY**

| S | M | T | W | T | F | S |
|---|---|---|---|---|---|---|
|   |   |   |   |   |   | 1 |
| 2 | 3 | 4 | 5 | 6 | 7 | 8 |
| 9 | 10 | 11 | 12 | 13 | 14 | 15 |
| 16 | 17 | 18 | 19 | 20 | 21 | 22 |
| 23 | 24 | 25 | 26 | 27 | 28 | 29 |
| 30 | 31 |   |   |   |   |   |

**JUNE**

| S | M | T | W | T | F | S |
|---|---|---|---|---|---|---|
|   |   |   |   | 1 | 2 | 3 |
| 4 | 5 | 6 | 7 | 8 | 9 | 10 |
| 11 | 12 | 13 | 14 | 15 | 16 | 17 |
| 18 | 19 | 20 | 21 | 22 | 23 | 24 |
| 25 | 26 | 27 | 28 | 29 | 30 |   |

**AUGUST**

| S | M | T | W | T | F | S |
|---|---|---|---|---|---|---|
|   |   | 1 | 2 | 3 | 4 | 5 |
| 6 | 7 | 8 | 9 | 10 | 11 | 12 |
| 13 | 14 | 15 | 16 | 17 | 18 | 19 |
| 20 | 21 | 22 | 23 | 24 | 25 | 26 |
| 27 | 28 | 29 | 30 | 31 |   |   |

Mount Dana and Mount Gibbs,
Tuolumne River, Yosemite National Park,
California, 1944

West Slope of Mount Whitney, Sierra Nevada, California, c. 1932

# JULY

| **24** MONDAY ◑ | **25** TUESDAY | **26** WEDNESDAY |
|---|---|---|
| a.m. | a.m. | a.m. |
| p.m. | p.m. | p.m. |

| **27** THURSDAY | **28** FRIDAY | **29** SATURDAY |
|---|---|---|
| a.m. | a.m. | |
| p.m. | p.m. | **30** SUNDAY ● |

# JULY / AUGUST

## 31 MONDAY
a.m.

p.m.

## 1 TUESDAY
a.m.

p.m.

## 2 WEDNESDAY
a.m.

p.m.

## 3 THURSDAY
a.m.

p.m.

## 4 FRIDAY
a.m.

p.m.

## 5 SATURDAY

## 6 SUNDAY

**AUGUST**

| S | M | T | W | T | F | S |
|---|---|---|---|---|---|---|
|   |   | 1 | 2 | 3 | 4 | 5 |
| 6 | 7 | 8 | 9 | 10 | 11 | 12 |
| 13 | 14 | 15 | 16 | 17 | 18 | 19 |
| 20 | 21 | 22 | 23 | 24 | 25 | 26 |
| 27 | 28 | 29 | 30 | 31 |   |   |

**JULY**

| S | M | T | W | T | F | S |
|---|---|---|---|---|---|---|
|   |   |   |   |   |   | 1 |
| 2 | 3 | 4 | 5 | 6 | 7 | 8 |
| 9 | 10 | 11 | 12 | 13 | 14 | 15 |
| 16 | 17 | 18 | 19 | 20 | 21 | 22 |
| 23 | 24 | 25 | 26 | 27 | 28 | 29 |
| 30 | 31 |   |   |   |   |   |

**SEPTEMBER**

| S | M | T | W | T | F | S |
|---|---|---|---|---|---|---|
|   |   |   |   |   | 1 | 2 |
| 3 | 4 | 5 | 6 | 7 | 8 | 9 |
| 10 | 11 | 12 | 13 | 14 | 15 | 16 |
| 17 | 18 | 19 | 20 | 21 | 22 | 23 |
| 24 | 25 | 26 | 27 | 28 | 29 | 30 |

Sand Dunes, Oceano, California,
c. 1950

Sand Bar, Rio Grande, Big Bend National Park, Texas, 1947

# AUGUST

## 7 MONDAY

a.m.

p.m.

Civic Holiday (Canada)

## 8 TUESDAY

a.m.

p.m.

## 9 WEDNESDAY

a.m.

p.m.

## 10 THURSDAY

a.m.

p.m.

## 11 FRIDAY

a.m.

p.m.

## 12 SATURDAY

## 13 SUNDAY

**AUGUST**

| S | M | T | W | T | F | S |
|---|---|---|---|---|---|---|
|   |   | 1 | 2 | 3 | 4 | 5 |
| 6 | 7 | 8 | 9 | 10 | 11 | 12 |
| 13 | 14 | 15 | 16 | 17 | 18 | 19 |
| 20 | 21 | 22 | 23 | 24 | 25 | 26 |
| 27 | 28 | 29 | 30 | 31 |   |   |

**JULY**

| S | M | T | W | T | F | S |
|---|---|---|---|---|---|---|
|   |   |   |   |   |   | 1 |
| 2 | 3 | 4 | 5 | 6 | 7 | 8 |
| 9 | 10 | 11 | 12 | 13 | 14 | 15 |
| 16 | 17 | 18 | 19 | 20 | 21 | 22 |
| 23 | 24 | 25 | 26 | 27 | 28 | 29 |
| 30 | 31 |   |   |   |   |   |

**SEPTEMBER**

| S | M | T | W | T | F | S |
|---|---|---|---|---|---|---|
|   |   |   |   |   | 1 | 2 |
| 3 | 4 | 5 | 6 | 7 | 8 | 9 |
| 10 | 11 | 12 | 13 | 14 | 15 | 16 |
| 17 | 18 | 19 | 20 | 21 | 22 | 23 |
| 24 | 25 | 26 | 27 | 28 | 29 | 30 |

# AUGUST

**14** MONDAY

a.m.

p.m.

**15** TUESDAY ○

a.m.

p.m.

**16** WEDNESDAY

a.m.

p.m.

**17** THURSDAY

a.m.

p.m.

**18** FRIDAY

a.m.

p.m.

**19** SATURDAY

**20** SUNDAY

Old Faithful Geyser, Late Evening,
Yellowstone National Park, Wyoming, 1942

Nipomo Dunes, California, 1963

# AUGUST

**21** MONDAY

a.m.

p.m.

**22** TUESDAY ◑

a.m.

p.m.

**23** WEDNESDAY

a.m.

p.m.

**24** THURSDAY

a.m.

p.m.

**25** FRIDAY

a.m.

p.m.

**26** SATURDAY

**27** SUNDAY

# AUGUST / SEPTEMBER

**28** MONDAY

a.m.

p.m.

**29** TUESDAY ●

a.m.

p.m.

**30** WEDNESDAY

a.m.

p.m.

**31** THURSDAY

a.m.

p.m.

**1** FRIDAY

a.m.

p.m.

**2** SATURDAY

**3** SUNDAY

# SEPTEMBER

**4** MONDAY

a.m.

p.m.

Labor Day

**5** TUESDAY ◑

a.m.

p.m.

**6** WEDNESDAY

a.m.

p.m.

**7** THURSDAY

a.m.

p.m.

**8** FRIDAY

a.m.

p.m.

**9** SATURDAY

**10** SUNDAY

**SEPTEMBER**

| S | M | T | W | T | F | S |
|---|---|---|---|---|---|---|
|   |   |   |   |   | 1 | 2 |
| 3 | 4 | 5 | 6 | 7 | 8 | 9 |
| 10 | 11 | 12 | 13 | 14 | 15 | 16 |
| 17 | 18 | 19 | 20 | 21 | 22 | 23 |
| 24 | 25 | 26 | 27 | 28 | 29 | 30 |

**AUGUST**

| S | M | T | W | T | F | S |
|---|---|---|---|---|---|---|
|   |   | 1 | 2 | 3 | 4 | 5 |
| 6 | 7 | 8 | 9 | 10 | 11 | 12 |
| 13 | 14 | 15 | 16 | 17 | 18 | 19 |
| 20 | 21 | 22 | 23 | 24 | 25 | 26 |
| 27 | 28 | 29 | 30 | 31 |   |   |

**OCTOBER**

| S | M | T | W | T | F | S |
|---|---|---|---|---|---|---|
| 1 | 2 | 3 | 4 | 5 | 6 | 7 |
| 8 | 9 | 10 | 11 | 12 | 13 | 14 |
| 15 | 16 | 17 | 18 | 19 | 20 | 21 |
| 22 | 23 | 24 | 25 | 26 | 27 | 28 |
| 29 | 30 | 31 |   |   |   |   |

# SEPTEMBER

**11** MONDAY

a.m.

p.m.

**12** TUESDAY

a.m.

p.m.

**13** WEDNESDAY ○

a.m.

p.m.

**14** THURSDAY

a.m.

p.m.

**15** FRIDAY

a.m.

p.m.

**16** SATURDAY

**17** SUNDAY

Half Dome, Oak Trees, Autumn, Yosemite National Park, California, 1938

Poplar Trees, Owens Valley,
California, c. 1943

# SEPTEMBER

**18** MONDAY

a.m.

p.m.

**19** TUESDAY

a.m.

p.m.

**20** WEDNESDAY ◑

a.m.

p.m.

**21** THURSDAY

a.m.

p.m.

**22** FRIDAY

a.m.

p.m.

Autumnal Equinox

**23** SATURDAY

**24** SUNDAY

**SEPTEMBER**

| S | M | T | W | T | F | S |
|---|---|---|---|---|---|---|
|   |   |   |   |   | 1 | 2 |
| 3 | 4 | 5 | 6 | 7 | 8 | 9 |
| 10 | 11 | 12 | 13 | 14 | 15 | 16 |
| 17 | 18 | 19 | 20 | 21 | 22 | 23 |
| 24 | 25 | 26 | 27 | 28 | 29 | 30 |

**AUGUST**

| S | M | T | W | T | F | S |
|---|---|---|---|---|---|---|
|   |   | 1 | 2 | 3 | 4 | 5 |
| 6 | 7 | 8 | 9 | 10 | 11 | 12 |
| 13 | 14 | 15 | 16 | 17 | 18 | 19 |
| 20 | 21 | 22 | 23 | 24 | 25 | 26 |
| 27 | 28 | 29 | 30 | 31 |   |   |

**OCTOBER**

| S | M | T | W | T | F | S |
|---|---|---|---|---|---|---|
| 1 | 2 | 3 | 4 | 5 | 6 | 7 |
| 8 | 9 | 10 | 11 | 12 | 13 | 14 |
| 15 | 16 | 17 | 18 | 19 | 20 | 21 |
| 22 | 23 | 24 | 25 | 26 | 27 | 28 |
| 29 | 30 | 31 |   |   |   |   |

# SEPTEMBER/OCTOBER

**25** MONDAY

a.m.

p.m.

**26** TUESDAY

a.m.

p.m.

**27** WEDNESDAY ●

a.m.

p.m.

**28** THURSDAY

a.m.

p.m.

**29** FRIDAY

a.m.

p.m.

**30** SATURDAY

*Rosh Hashanah*

**1** SUNDAY

**SEPTEMBER**

| S | M | T | W | T | F | S |
|---|---|---|---|---|---|---|
|   |   |   |   |   | 1 | 2 |
| 3 | 4 | 5 | 6 | 7 | 8 | 9 |
| 10 | 11 | 12 | 13 | 14 | 15 | 16 |
| 17 | 18 | 19 | 20 | 21 | 22 | 23 |
| 24 | 25 | 26 | 27 | 28 | 29 | 30 |

**AUGUST**

| S | M | T | W | T | F | S |
|---|---|---|---|---|---|---|
|   |   | 1 | 2 | 3 | 4 | 5 |
| 6 | 7 | 8 | 9 | 10 | 11 | 12 |
| 13 | 14 | 15 | 16 | 17 | 18 | 19 |
| 20 | 21 | 22 | 23 | 24 | 25 | 26 |
| 27 | 28 | 29 | 30 | 31 |   |   |

**OCTOBER**

| S | M | T | W | T | F | S |
|---|---|---|---|---|---|---|
| 1 | 2 | 3 | 4 | 5 | 6 | 7 |
| 8 | 9 | 10 | 11 | 12 | 13 | 14 |
| 15 | 16 | 17 | 18 | 19 | 20 | 21 |
| 22 | 23 | 24 | 25 | 26 | 27 | 28 |
| 29 | 30 | 31 |   |   |   |   |

Merced River, Cliffs, Autumn, Yosemite National Park, California, c. 1939

Leaves, Frost, Stump, October Morning, Yosemite National Park, California, c. 1931

# OCTOBER

**2** MONDAY
a.m.

p.m.

**3** TUESDAY
a.m.

p.m.

**4** WEDNESDAY
a.m.

p.m.

**5** THURSDAY
a.m.

FLU

p.m.

**6** FRIDAY
a.m.

p.m.

**7** SATURDAY

**8** SUNDAY

**OCTOBER**

| S | M | T | W | T | F | S |
|---|---|---|---|---|---|---|
| 1 | 2 | 3 | 4 | 5 | 6 | 7 |
| 8 | 9 | 10 | 11 | 12 | 13 | 14 |
| 15 | 16 | 17 | 18 | 19 | 20 | 21 |
| 22 | 23 | 24 | 25 | 26 | 27 | 28 |
| 29 | 30 | 31 | | | | |

**SEPTEMBER**

| S | M | T | W | T | F | S |
|---|---|---|---|---|---|---|
| | | | | | 1 | 2 |
| 3 | 4 | 5 | 6 | 7 | 8 | 9 |
| 10 | 11 | 12 | 13 | 14 | 15 | 16 |
| 17 | 18 | 19 | 20 | 21 | 22 | 23 |
| 24 | 25 | 26 | 27 | 28 | 29 | 30 |

**NOVEMBER**

| S | M | T | W | T | F | S |
|---|---|---|---|---|---|---|
| | | | 1 | 2 | 3 | 4 |
| 5 | 6 | 7 | 8 | 9 | 10 | 11 |
| 12 | 13 | 14 | 15 | 16 | 17 | 18 |
| 19 | 20 | 21 | 22 | 23 | 24 | 25 |
| 26 | 27 | 28 | 29 | 30 | | |

# OCTOBER

**9** MONDAY

a.m.

p.m.

Columbus Day Observed

Thanksgiving Day (Canada)

Yom Kippur

**10** TUESDAY

a.m.

p.m.

**11** WEDNESDAY

a.m.

p.m.

**12** THURSDAY

a.m.

p.m.

**13** FRIDAY ○

a.m.

p.m.

**14** SATURDAY

**15** SUNDAY

**OCTOBER**

| S | M | T | W | T | F | S |
|---|---|---|---|---|---|---|
| 1 | 2 | 3 | 4 | 5 | 6 | 7 |
| 8 | 9 | 10 | 11 | 12 | 13 | 14 |
| 15 | 16 | 17 | 18 | 19 | 20 | 21 |
| 22 | 23 | 24 | 25 | 26 | 27 | 28 |
| 29 | 30 | 31 | | | | |

**SEPTEMBER**

| S | M | T | W | T | F | S |
|---|---|---|---|---|---|---|
| | | | | | 1 | 2 |
| 3 | 4 | 5 | 6 | 7 | 8 | 9 |
| 10 | 11 | 12 | 13 | 14 | 15 | 16 |
| 17 | 18 | 19 | 20 | 21 | 22 | 23 |
| 24 | 25 | 26 | 27 | 28 | 29 | 30 |

**NOVEMBER**

| S | M | T | W | T | F | S |
|---|---|---|---|---|---|---|
| | | | 1 | 2 | 3 | 4 |
| 5 | 6 | 7 | 8 | 9 | 10 | 11 |
| 12 | 13 | 14 | 15 | 16 | 17 | 18 |
| 19 | 20 | 21 | 22 | 23 | 24 | 25 |
| 26 | 27 | 28 | 29 | 30 | | |

Aspens, Northern New Mexico, 1958

Dawn, Autumn, Great Smoky Mountains
National Park, Tennessee, 1948

# OCTOBER

## 16 MONDAY
a.m.

p.m.

## 17 TUESDAY
a.m.

p.m.

## 18 WEDNESDAY
a.m.

p.m.

## 19 THURSDAY
a.m.

p.m.

## 20 FRIDAY ◑
a.m.

p.m.

## 21 SATURDAY
a.m.

## 22 SUNDAY

# OCTOBER

## 23 MONDAY
a.m.

p.m.

## 24 TUESDAY
a.m.

p.m.

## 25 WEDNESDAY
a.m.

p.m.

## 26 THURSDAY
a.m.

p.m.

## 27 FRIDAY ●
a.m.

p.m.

## 28 SATURDAY

## 29 SUNDAY

Daylight Saving Time ends

**OCTOBER**

| S | M | T | W | T | F | S |
|---|---|---|---|---|---|---|
| 1 | 2 | 3 | 4 | 5 | 6 | 7 |
| 8 | 9 | 10 | 11 | 12 | 13 | 14 |
| 15 | 16 | 17 | 18 | 19 | 20 | 21 |
| 22 | 23 | 24 | 25 | 26 | 27 | 28 |
| 29 | 30 | 31 | | | | |

**SEPTEMBER**

| S | M | T | W | T | F | S |
|---|---|---|---|---|---|---|
| | | | | | 1 | 2 |
| 3 | 4 | 5 | 6 | 7 | 8 | 9 |
| 10 | 11 | 12 | 13 | 14 | 15 | 16 |
| 17 | 18 | 19 | 20 | 21 | 22 | 23 |
| 24 | 25 | 26 | 27 | 28 | 29 | 30 |

**NOVEMBER**

| S | M | T | W | T | F | S |
|---|---|---|---|---|---|---|
| | | | 1 | 2 | 3 | 4 |
| 5 | 6 | 7 | 8 | 9 | 10 | 11 |
| 12 | 13 | 14 | 15 | 16 | 17 | 18 |
| 19 | 20 | 21 | 22 | 23 | 24 | 25 |
| 26 | 27 | 28 | 29 | 30 | | |

Silverton, Colorado, 1951

Autumn Moon, High Sierra from Glacier Point, Yosemite National Park, California, 1948

# OCTOBER / NOVEMBER

**30** MONDAY

a.m.

p.m.

**31** TUESDAY

a.m.

p.m.

Halloween

**1** WEDNESDAY

a.m.

p.m.

**2** THURSDAY

a.m.

p.m.

**3** FRIDAY

a.m.

p.m.

**4** SATURDAY

**5** SUNDAY

**OCTOBER**
| S | M | T | W | T | F | S |
|---|---|---|---|---|---|---|
| 1 | 2 | 3 | 4 | 5 | 6 | 7 |
| 8 | 9 | 10 | 11 | 12 | 13 | 14 |
| 15 | 16 | 17 | 18 | 19 | 20 | 21 |
| 22 | 23 | 24 | 25 | 26 | 27 | 28 |
| 29 | 30 | 31 | | | | |

**SEPTEMBER**
| S | M | T | W | T | F | S |
|---|---|---|---|---|---|---|
| | | | | | 1 | 2 |
| 3 | 4 | 5 | 6 | 7 | 8 | 9 |
| 10 | 11 | 12 | 13 | 14 | 15 | 16 |
| 17 | 18 | 19 | 20 | 21 | 22 | 23 |
| 24 | 25 | 26 | 27 | 28 | 29 | 30 |

**NOVEMBER**
| S | M | T | W | T | F | S |
|---|---|---|---|---|---|---|
| | | | | 1 | 2 | 3 | 4 |
| 5 | 6 | 7 | 8 | 9 | 10 | 11 |
| 12 | 13 | 14 | 15 | 16 | 17 | 18 |
| 19 | 20 | 21 | 22 | 23 | 24 | 25 |
| 26 | 27 | 28 | 29 | 30 | | |

# NOVEMBER

**6** MONDAY

a.m.

p.m.

**7** TUESDAY

a.m.

p.m.

Election Day

**8** WEDNESDAY

a.m.

p.m.

**9** THURSDAY

a.m.

p.m.

**10** FRIDAY

a.m.

p.m.

**11** SATURDAY ◯

Veterans Day

Remembrance Day (Canada)

**12** SUNDAY

**NOVEMBER**

| S | M | T | W | T | F | S |
|---|---|---|---|---|---|---|
|   |   |   | 1 | 2 | 3 | 4 |
| 5 | 6 | 7 | 8 | 9 | 10 | 11 |
| 12 | 13 | 14 | 15 | 16 | 17 | 18 |
| 19 | 20 | 21 | 22 | 23 | 24 | 25 |
| 26 | 27 | 28 | 29 | 30 |   |   |

**OCTOBER**

| S | M | T | W | T | F | S |
|---|---|---|---|---|---|---|
| 1 | 2 | 3 | 4 | 5 | 6 | 7 |
| 8 | 9 | 10 | 11 | 12 | 13 | 14 |
| 15 | 16 | 17 | 18 | 19 | 20 | 21 |
| 22 | 23 | 24 | 25 | 26 | 27 | 28 |
| 29 | 30 | 31 |   |   |   |   |

**DECEMBER**

| S | M | T | W | T | F | S |
|---|---|---|---|---|---|---|
|   |   |   |   |   | 1 | 2 |
| 3 | 4 | 5 | 6 | 7 | 8 | 9 |
| 10 | 11 | 12 | 13 | 14 | 15 | 16 |
| 17 | 18 | 19 | 20 | 21 | 22 | 23 |
| 24 | 25 | 26 | 27 | 28 | 29 | 30 |
| 31 |   |   |   |   |   |   |

Santa Elena Canyon, Big Bend National Park, Texas, 1947

Grand Canyon from Yavapai Point, Grand
Canyon National Park, Arizona, 1942

# NOVEMBER

**13** MONDAY

a.m.

p.m.

**14** TUESDAY

a.m.

p.m.

**15** WEDNESDAY

a.m.

p.m.

**16** THURSDAY

a.m.

p.m.

**17** FRIDAY

a.m.

p.m.

**18** SATURDAY

**19** SUNDAY

# NOVEMBER

**20** MONDAY

a.m.

p.m.

**21** TUESDAY

a.m.

p.m.

**22** WEDNESDAY

a.m.

p.m.

**23** THURSDAY

a.m.

p.m.

Thanksgiving Day

**24** FRIDAY

a.m.

p.m.

**25** SATURDAY

**26** SUNDAY

Canyon de Chelly National Monument, Arizona, 1942

Sunrise, Mount Tom, Sierra Nevada, California, 1948

# NOVEMBER / DECEMBER

## 27 MONDAY

a.m.

p.m.

## 28 TUESDAY

a.m.

p.m.

## 29 WEDNESDAY

a.m.

p.m.

## 30 THURSDAY

a.m.

p.m.

## 1 FRIDAY

a.m.

p.m.

## 2 SATURDAY

## 3 SUNDAY

# DECEMBER

**4** MONDAY

a.m.

p.m.

**5** TUESDAY

a.m.

p.m.

**6** WEDNESDAY

a.m.

p.m.

**7** THURSDAY

a.m.

p.m.

**8** FRIDAY

a.m.

p.m.

**9** SATURDAY

**10** SUNDAY

**DECEMBER**

| S | M | T | W | T | F | S |
|---|---|---|---|---|---|---|
|   |   |   |   |   | 1 | 2 |
| 3 | 4 | 5 | 6 | 7 | 8 | 9 |
| 10 | 11 | 12 | 13 | 14 | 15 | 16 |
| 17 | 18 | 19 | 20 | 21 | 22 | 23 |
| 24 | 25 | 26 | 27 | 28 | 29 | 30 |
| 31 |   |   |   |   |   |   |

**NOVEMBER**

| S | M | T | W | T | F | S |
|---|---|---|---|---|---|---|
|   |   |   | 1 | 2 | 3 | 4 |
| 5 | 6 | 7 | 8 | 9 | 10 | 11 |
| 12 | 13 | 14 | 15 | 16 | 17 | 18 |
| 19 | 20 | 21 | 22 | 23 | 24 | 25 |
| 26 | 27 | 28 | 29 | 30 |   |   |

**JANUARY**

| S | M | T | W | T | F | S |
|---|---|---|---|---|---|---|
| 1 | 2 | 3 | 4 | 5 | 6 |   |
| 7 | 8 | 9 | 10 | 11 | 12 | 13 |
| 14 | 15 | 16 | 17 | 18 | 19 | 20 |
| 21 | 22 | 23 | 24 | 25 | 26 | 27 |
| 28 | 29 | 30 | 31 |   |   |   |

El Capitan, Winter, Sunrise, Yosemite
National Park, California, 1968

Trees and Cliffs of Eagle Peak, Winter, Yosemite National Park, California, c. 1935

# DECEMBER

**11** MONDAY ○

a.m.

p.m.

**12** TUESDAY

a.m.

p.m.

**13** WEDNESDAY

a.m.

p.m.

**14** THURSDAY

a.m.

p.m.

**15** FRIDAY

a.m.

p.m.

**16** SATURDAY

**17** SUNDAY ◑

# DECEMBER

**18** MONDAY

a.m.

p.m.

**19** TUESDAY

a.m.

p.m.

**20** WEDNESDAY

a.m.

p.m.

**21** THURSDAY

a.m.

p.m.

Winter Solstice

**22** FRIDAY

a.m.

p.m.

Hanukkah

**23** SATURDAY

**24** SUNDAY

**DECEMBER**
S M T W T F S
1 2
3 4 5 6 7 8 9
10 11 12 13 14 15 16
17 18 19 20 21 22 23
24 25 26 27 28 29 30
31

**NOVEMBER**
S M T W T F S
1 2 3 4
5 6 7 8 9 10 11
12 13 14 15 16 17 18
19 20 21 22 23 24 25
26 27 28 29 30

**JANUARY**
S M T W T F S
1 2 3 4 5 6
7 8 9 10 11 12 13
14 15 16 17 18 19 20
21 22 23 24 25 26 27
28 29 30 31

Mount Galen Clark, Yosemite
National Park, California, 1927

Mount McKinley and Wonder Lake, Denali National Park, Alaska, 1947

# DECEMBER

**25** MONDAY

a.m.

p.m.

Christmas

**26** TUESDAY

a.m.

p.m.

Boxing Day (Canada)

**27** WEDNESDAY

a.m.

p.m.

**28** THURSDAY

a.m.

p.m.

**29** FRIDAY

a.m.

p.m.

**30** SATURDAY

**31** SUNDAY

**DECEMBER**

| S | M | T | W | T | F | S |
|---|---|---|---|---|---|---|
|   |   |   |   |   | 1 | 2 |
| 3 | 4 | 5 | 6 | 7 | 8 | 9 |
| 10 | 11 | 12 | 13 | 14 | 15 | 16 |
| 17 | 18 | 19 | 20 | 21 | 22 | 23 |
| 24 | 25 | 26 | 27 | 28 | 29 | 30 |
| 31 |   |   |   |   |   |   |

**NOVEMBER**

| S | M | T | W | T | F | S |
|---|---|---|---|---|---|---|
|   |   |   | 1 | 2 | 3 | 4 |
| 5 | 6 | 7 | 8 | 9 | 10 | 11 |
| 12 | 13 | 14 | 15 | 16 | 17 | 18 |
| 19 | 20 | 21 | 22 | 23 | 24 | 25 |
| 26 | 27 | 28 | 29 | 30 |   |   |

**JANUARY**

| S | M | T | W | T | F | S |
|---|---|---|---|---|---|---|
|   | 1 | 2 | 3 | 4 | 5 | 6 |
| 7 | 8 | 9 | 10 | 11 | 12 | 13 |
| 14 | 15 | 16 | 17 | 18 | 19 | 20 |
| 21 | 22 | 23 | 24 | 25 | 26 | 27 |
| 28 | 29 | 30 | 31 |   |   |   |

# JANUARY 2000

| MONDAY | TUESDAY | WEDNESDAY | THURSDAY | FRIDAY | SAT/SUN |
|--------|---------|-----------|----------|--------|---------|
| | | | | | **1 / 2**<br>1 New Year's Day |
| **3** | **4** | **5** | **6** | **7** | **8 / 9** |
| **10** | **11** | **12** | **13** | **14** | **15 / 16** |
| **17**<br>Martin Luther King Jr. Day | **18** | **19** | **20** | **21** | **22 / 23** |
| **24** | **25** | **26** | **27** | **28** | **29 / 30** |
| **31** | | | | | |

# FEBRUARY 2000

| MONDAY | TUESDAY | WEDNESDAY | THURSDAY | FRIDAY | SAT/SUN |
|---|---|---|---|---|---|
|  | 1 | 2 | 3 | 4 | 5 / 6 |
| 7 | 8 | 9 | 10 | 11 | 12 / 13<br>12 Lincoln's Birthday |
| 14<br>Valentine's Day | 15 | 16 | 17 | 18 | 19 / 20 |
| 21<br>Presidents' Day | 22<br>Washington's Birthday | 23 | 24 | 25 | 26 / 27 |
| 28 | 29 |  |  |  |  |
|  |  |  |  |  |  |

# MARCH 2000

| MONDAY | TUESDAY | WEDNESDAY | THURSDAY | FRIDAY | SAT/SUN |
|---|---|---|---|---|---|
| | | 1 | 2 | 3 | 4 / 5 |
| 6 | 7 | 8<br><br>Ash Wednesday | 9 | 10 | 11 / 12 |
| 13 | 14 | 15 | 16 | 17<br><br>St. Patrick's Day | 18 / 19 |
| 20<br><br>Vernal Equinox | 21 | 22 | 23 | 24 | 25 / 26 |
| 27 | 28 | 29 | 30 | 31 | |
| | | | | | |

# APRIL 2000

| MONDAY | TUESDAY | WEDNESDAY | THURSDAY | FRIDAY | SAT/SUN |
|--------|---------|-----------|----------|--------|---------|
|  |  |  |  |  | **1 / 2**<br>2 Daylight Saving<br>Time begins |
| 3 | 4 | 5 | 6 | 7 | **8 / 9** |
| 10 | 11 | 12 | 13 | 14 | **15 / 16**<br>16 Palm Sunday |
| 17 | 18 | 19 | **20**<br>Passover | **21**<br>Good Friday | **22 / 23**<br>22 Earth Day<br>23 Easter Sunday |
| 24 | 25 | 26 | 27 | 28 | **29 / 30** |
|  |  |  |  |  |  |

# MAY 2000

| MONDAY | TUESDAY | WEDNESDAY | THURSDAY | FRIDAY | SAT/SUN |
|---|---|---|---|---|---|
| 1 | 2 | 3 | 4 | 5 | 6 / 7 |
| 8 | 9 | 10 | 11 | 12 | 13 / 14<br><br>14 Mother's Day |
| 15 | 16 | 17 | 18 | 19 | 20 / 21 |
| 22<br><br>Victoria Day (Canada) | 23 | 24 | 25 | 26 | 27 / 28 |
| 29<br><br>Memorial Day<br>Observed | 30<br><br>Memorial Day | 31 | | | |
| | | | | | |

# JUNE 2000

| MONDAY | TUESDAY | WEDNESDAY | THURSDAY | FRIDAY | SAT/SUN |
|--------|---------|-----------|----------|--------|---------|
| | | | 1 | 2 | 3 / 4 |
| 5 | 6 | 7 | 8 | 9 | 10 / 11 |
| 12 | 13 | 14 <br> Flag Day | 15 | 16 | 17 / 18 <br> 18 Father's Day |
| 19 | 20 <br> Summer Solstice | 21 | 22 | 23 | 24 / 25 |
| 26 | 27 | 28 | 29 | 30 | |
| | | | | | |

# JULY 2000

| MONDAY | TUESDAY | WEDNESDAY | THURSDAY | FRIDAY | SAT/SUN |
|--------|---------|-----------|----------|--------|---------|
|  |  |  |  |  | **1 / 2**<br>1 Canada Day<br>(Canada) |
| **3** | **4**<br>Independence Day | **5** | **6** | **7** | **8 / 9** |
| **10** | **11** | **12** | **13** | **14** | **15 / 16** |
| **17** | **18** | **19** | **20** | **21** | **22 / 23** |
| **24** | **25** | **26** | **27** | **28** | **29 / 30** |
| **31** |  |  |  |  |  |

# AUGUST 2000

| MONDAY | TUESDAY | WEDNESDAY | THURSDAY | FRIDAY | SAT/SUN |
|---|---|---|---|---|---|
|  | 1 | 2 | 3 | 4 | 5 / 6 |
| 7<br>Civic Holiday (Canada) | 8 | 9 | 10 | 11 | 12 / 13 |
| 14 | 15 | 16 | 17 | 18 | 19 / 20 |
| 21 | 22 | 23 | 24 | 25 | 26 / 27 |
| 28 | 29 | 30 | 31 |  |  |
|  |  |  |  |  |  |

# SEPTEMBER 2000

| MONDAY | TUESDAY | WEDNESDAY | THURSDAY | FRIDAY | SAT/SUN |
|--------|---------|-----------|----------|--------|---------|
|  |  |  |  | 1 | 2 / 3 |
| 4<br>Labor Day | 5 | 6 | 7 | 8 | 9 / 10 |
| 11 | 12 | 13 | 14 | 15 | 16 / 17 |
| 18 | 19 | 20 | 21 | 22<br>Autumnal Equinox | 23 / 24 |
| 25 | 26 | 27 | 28 | 29 | 30<br>Rosh Hashanah |
|  |  |  |  |  |  |

# OCTOBER 2000

| MONDAY | TUESDAY | WEDNESDAY | THURSDAY | FRIDAY | SAT/SUN |
|---|---|---|---|---|---|
| | | | | | **1** |
| **2** | **3** | **4** | **5** | **6** | **7 / 8** |
| **9**<br>Columbus Day Observed<br>Thanksgiving Day<br>(Canada)<br>Yom Kippur | **10** | **11** | **12** | **13** | **14 / 15** |
| **16** | **17** | **18** | **19** | **20** | **21 / 22** |
| **23** | **24** | **25** | **26** | **27** | **28 / 29**<br>29 Daylight Saving<br>Time ends |
| **30** | **31**<br>Halloween | | | | |

# NOVEMBER 2000

| MONDAY | TUESDAY | WEDNESDAY | THURSDAY | FRIDAY | SAT/SUN |
|---|---|---|---|---|---|
| | | 1 | 2 | 3 | 4 / 5 |
| 6 | 7<br><br>Election Day | 8 | 9 | 10 | 11 / 12<br><br>11 Veterans Day<br>11 Remembrance Day<br>(Canada) |
| 13 | 14 | 15 | 16 | 17 | 18 / 19 |
| 20 | 21 | 22 | 23<br><br>Thanksgiving Day | 24 | 25 / 26 |
| 27 | 28 | 29 | 30 | | |
| | | | | | |

# DECEMBER 2000

| MONDAY | TUESDAY | WEDNESDAY | THURSDAY | FRIDAY | SAT/SUN |
|--------|---------|-----------|----------|--------|---------|
| | | | | 1 | 2 / 3 |
| 4 | 5 | 6 | 7 | 8 | 9 / 10 |
| 11 | 12 | 13 | 14 | 15 | 16 / 17 |
| 18 | 19 | 20 | 21<br>Winter Solstice | 22<br>Hanukkah | 23 / 24 |
| 25<br>Christmas | 26<br>Boxing Day (Canada) | 27 | 28 | 29 | 30 / 31 |
| | | | | | |

# JANUARY 2001

| MONDAY | TUESDAY | WEDNESDAY | THURSDAY | FRIDAY | SAT/SUN |
|--------|---------|-----------|----------|--------|---------|
| **1**<br>New Year's Day | **2** | **3** | **4** | **5** | **6 / 7** |
| **8** | **9** | **10** | **11** | **12** | **13 / 14** |
| **15**<br>Martin Luther King Jr. Day | **16** | **17** | **18** | **19** | **20 / 21** |
| **22** | **23** | **24** | **25** | **26** | **27 / 28** |
| **29** | **30** | **31** | | | |
| | | | | | |

# FEBRUARY 2001

| MONDAY | TUESDAY | WEDNESDAY | THURSDAY | FRIDAY | SAT/SUN |
|--------|---------|-----------|----------|--------|---------|
| | | | 1 | 2 | 3 / 4 |
| 5 | 6 | 7 | 8 | 9 | 10 / 11 |
| 12<br>Lincoln's Birthday | 13 | 14<br>Valentine's Day | 15 | 16 | 17 / 18 |
| 19<br>Presidents' Day | 20 | 21 | 22<br>Washington's Birthday | 23 | 24 / 25 |
| 26 | 27 | 28 | | | |
| | | | | | |

# 2000

## JANUARY
| S | M | T | W | T | F | S |
|---|---|---|---|---|---|---|
|   |   |   |   |   |   | 1 |
| 2 | 3 | 4 | 5 | 6 | 7 | 8 |
| 9 | 10 | 11 | 12 | 13 | 14 | 15 |
| 16 | 17 | 18 | 19 | 20 | 21 | 22 |
| 23 | 24 | 25 | 26 | 27 | 28 | 29 |
| 30 | 31 |   |   |   |   |   |

## FEBRUARY
| S | M | T | W | T | F | S |
|---|---|---|---|---|---|---|
|   |   | 1 | 2 | 3 | 4 | 5 |
| 6 | 7 | 8 | 9 | 10 | 11 | 12 |
| 13 | 14 | 15 | 16 | 17 | 18 | 19 |
| 20 | 21 | 22 | 23 | 24 | 25 | 26 |
| 27 | 28 | 29 |   |   |   |   |

## MARCH
| S | M | T | W | T | F | S |
|---|---|---|---|---|---|---|
|   |   |   | 1 | 2 | 3 | 4 |
| 5 | 6 | 7 | 8 | 9 | 10 | 11 |
| 12 | 13 | 14 | 15 | 16 | 17 | 18 |
| 19 | 20 | 21 | 22 | 23 | 24 | 25 |
| 26 | 27 | 28 | 29 | 30 | 31 |   |

## APRIL
| S | M | T | W | T | F | S |
|---|---|---|---|---|---|---|
|   |   |   |   |   |   | 1 |
| 2 | 3 | 4 | 5 | 6 | 7 | 8 |
| 9 | 10 | 11 | 12 | 13 | 14 | 15 |
| 16 | 17 | 18 | 19 | 20 | 21 | 22 |
| 23 | 24 | 25 | 26 | 27 | 28 | 29 |
| 30 |   |   |   |   |   |   |

## MAY
| S | M | T | W | T | F | S |
|---|---|---|---|---|---|---|
|   | 1 | 2 | 3 | 4 | 5 | 6 |
| 7 | 8 | 9 | 10 | 11 | 12 | 13 |
| 14 | 15 | 16 | 17 | 18 | 19 | 20 |
| 21 | 22 | 23 | 24 | 25 | 26 | 27 |
| 28 | 29 | 30 | 31 |   |   |   |

## JUNE
| S | M | T | W | T | F | S |
|---|---|---|---|---|---|---|
|   |   |   |   | 1 | 2 | 3 |
| 4 | 5 | 6 | 7 | 8 | 9 | 10 |
| 11 | 12 | 13 | 14 | 15 | 16 | 17 |
| 18 | 19 | 20 | 21 | 22 | 23 | 24 |
| 25 | 26 | 27 | 28 | 29 | 30 |   |

## JULY
| S | M | T | W | T | F | S |
|---|---|---|---|---|---|---|
|   |   |   |   |   |   | 1 |
| 2 | 3 | 4 | 5 | 6 | 7 | 8 |
| 9 | 10 | 11 | 12 | 13 | 14 | 15 |
| 16 | 17 | 18 | 19 | 20 | 21 | 22 |
| 23 | 24 | 25 | 26 | 27 | 28 | 29 |
| 30 | 31 |   |   |   |   |   |

## AUGUST
| S | M | T | W | T | F | S |
|---|---|---|---|---|---|---|
|   |   | 1 | 2 | 3 | 4 | 5 |
| 6 | 7 | 8 | 9 | 10 | 11 | 12 |
| 13 | 14 | 15 | 16 | 17 | 18 | 19 |
| 20 | 21 | 22 | 23 | 24 | 25 | 26 |
| 27 | 28 | 29 | 30 | 31 |   |   |

## SEPTEMBER
| S | M | T | W | T | F | S |
|---|---|---|---|---|---|---|
|   |   |   |   |   | 1 | 2 |
| 3 | 4 | 5 | 6 | 7 | 8 | 9 |
| 10 | 11 | 12 | 13 | 14 | 15 | 16 |
| 17 | 18 | 19 | 20 | 21 | 22 | 23 |
| 24 | 25 | 26 | 27 | 28 | 29 | 30 |

## OCTOBER
| S | M | T | W | T | F | S |
|---|---|---|---|---|---|---|
| 1 | 2 | 3 | 4 | 5 | 6 | 7 |
| 8 | 9 | 10 | 11 | 12 | 13 | 14 |
| 15 | 16 | 17 | 18 | 19 | 20 | 21 |
| 22 | 23 | 24 | 25 | 26 | 27 | 28 |
| 29 | 30 | 31 |   |   |   |   |

## NOVEMBER
| S | M | T | W | T | F | S |
|---|---|---|---|---|---|---|
|   |   |   | 1 | 2 | 3 | 4 |
| 5 | 6 | 7 | 8 | 9 | 10 | 11 |
| 12 | 13 | 14 | 15 | 16 | 17 | 18 |
| 19 | 20 | 21 | 22 | 23 | 24 | 25 |
| 26 | 27 | 28 | 29 | 30 |   |   |

## DECEMBER
| S | M | T | W | T | F | S |
|---|---|---|---|---|---|---|
|   |   |   |   |   | 1 | 2 |
| 3 | 4 | 5 | 6 | 7 | 8 | 9 |
| 10 | 11 | 12 | 13 | 14 | 15 | 16 |
| 17 | 18 | 19 | 20 | 21 | 22 | 23 |
| 24 | 25 | 26 | 27 | 28 | 29 | 30 |
| 31 |   |   |   |   |   |   |

# 2001

## JANUARY

| S | M | T | W | T | F | S |
|---|---|---|---|---|---|---|
| | 1 | 2 | 3 | 4 | 5 | 6 |
| 7 | 8 | 9 | 10 | 11 | 12 | 13 |
| 14 | 15 | 16 | 17 | 18 | 19 | 20 |
| 21 | 22 | 23 | 24 | 25 | 26 | 27 |
| 28 | 29 | 30 | 31 | | | |

## FEBRUARY

| S | M | T | W | T | F | S |
|---|---|---|---|---|---|---|
| | | | | 1 | 2 | 3 |
| 4 | 5 | 6 | 7 | 8 | 9 | 10 |
| 11 | 12 | 13 | 14 | 15 | 16 | 17 |
| 18 | 19 | 20 | 21 | 22 | 23 | 24 |
| 25 | 26 | 27 | 28 | | | |

## MARCH

| S | M | T | W | T | F | S |
|---|---|---|---|---|---|---|
| | | | | 1 | 2 | 3 |
| 4 | 5 | 6 | 7 | 8 | 9 | 10 |
| 11 | 12 | 13 | 14 | 15 | 16 | 17 |
| 18 | 19 | 20 | 21 | 22 | 23 | 24 |
| 25 | 26 | 27 | 28 | 29 | 30 | 31 |

## APRIL

| S | M | T | W | T | F | S |
|---|---|---|---|---|---|---|
| 1 | 2 | 3 | 4 | 5 | 6 | 7 |
| 8 | 9 | 10 | 11 | 12 | 13 | 14 |
| 15 | 16 | 17 | 18 | 19 | 20 | 21 |
| 22 | 23 | 24 | 25 | 26 | 27 | 28 |
| 29 | 30 | | | | | |

## MAY

| S | M | T | W | T | F | S |
|---|---|---|---|---|---|---|
| | | 1 | 2 | 3 | 4 | 5 |
| 6 | 7 | 8 | 9 | 10 | 11 | 12 |
| 13 | 14 | 15 | 16 | 17 | 18 | 19 |
| 20 | 21 | 22 | 23 | 24 | 25 | 26 |
| 27 | 28 | 29 | 30 | 31 | | |

## JUNE

| S | M | T | W | T | F | S |
|---|---|---|---|---|---|---|
| | | | | | 1 | 2 |
| 3 | 4 | 5 | 6 | 7 | 8 | 9 |
| 10 | 11 | 12 | 13 | 14 | 15 | 16 |
| 17 | 18 | 19 | 20 | 21 | 22 | 23 |
| 24 | 25 | 26 | 27 | 28 | 29 | 30 |

## JULY

| S | M | T | W | T | F | S |
|---|---|---|---|---|---|---|
| 1 | 2 | 3 | 4 | 5 | 6 | 7 |
| 8 | 9 | 10 | 11 | 12 | 13 | 14 |
| 15 | 16 | 17 | 18 | 19 | 20 | 21 |
| 22 | 23 | 24 | 25 | 26 | 27 | 28 |
| 29 | 30 | 31 | | | | |

## AUGUST

| S | M | T | W | T | F | S |
|---|---|---|---|---|---|---|
| | | | 1 | 2 | 3 | 4 |
| 5 | 6 | 7 | 8 | 9 | 10 | 11 |
| 12 | 13 | 14 | 15 | 16 | 17 | 18 |
| 19 | 20 | 21 | 22 | 23 | 24 | 25 |
| 26 | 27 | 28 | 29 | 30 | 31 | |

## SEPTEMBER

| S | M | T | W | T | F | S |
|---|---|---|---|---|---|---|
| | | | | | | 1 |
| 2 | 3 | 4 | 5 | 6 | 7 | 8 |
| 9 | 10 | 11 | 12 | 13 | 14 | 15 |
| 16 | 17 | 18 | 19 | 20 | 21 | 22 |
| 23 | 24 | 25 | 26 | 27 | 28 | 29 |
| 30 | | | | | | |

## OCTOBER

| S | M | T | W | T | F | S |
|---|---|---|---|---|---|---|
| | 1 | 2 | 3 | 4 | 5 | 6 |
| 7 | 8 | 9 | 10 | 11 | 12 | 13 |
| 14 | 15 | 16 | 17 | 18 | 19 | 20 |
| 21 | 22 | 23 | 24 | 25 | 26 | 27 |
| 28 | 29 | 30 | 31 | | | |

## NOVEMBER

| S | M | T | W | T | F | S |
|---|---|---|---|---|---|---|
| | | | | 1 | 2 | 3 |
| 4 | 5 | 6 | 7 | 8 | 9 | 10 |
| 11 | 12 | 13 | 14 | 15 | 16 | 17 |
| 18 | 19 | 20 | 21 | 22 | 23 | 24 |
| 25 | 26 | 27 | 28 | 29 | 30 | |

## DECEMBER

| S | M | T | W | T | F | S |
|---|---|---|---|---|---|---|
| | | | | | | 1 |
| 2 | 3 | 4 | 5 | 6 | 7 | 8 |
| 9 | 10 | 11 | 12 | 13 | 14 | 15 |
| 16 | 17 | 18 | 19 | 20 | 21 | 22 |
| 23 | 24 | 25 | 26 | 27 | 28 | 29 |
| 30 | 31 | | | | | |

# POSTERS BY ANSEL ADAMS

Recently, the bestselling Ansel Adams poster series was redesigned to create a fresh, contemporary look, with larger images and an elegant simplicity to the overall presentation. Sheet sizes were standardized so that commercially available poster frames can be used. The only thing that hasn't changed is the attention to quality – the superb duotone printing and heavy coated stock that have always been hallmarks of the series.

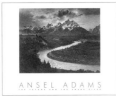
The Tetons and the
Snake River

Clearing Winter Storm

Cape Royal,
Grand Canyon

Mount McKinley and
Wonder Lake

Canyon de Chelly

Aspens

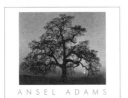
Oak Tree, Sunset City

Moonrise, Hernandez,
New Mexico

Redwoods

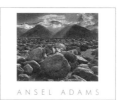
Tenaya Creek,
Dogwood, Rain

Mount Williamson

Winter Sunrise

Oak Tree,
Snowstorm

Moon and
Half Dome

Bridal Veil Fall

Sand Dunes,
Sunrise

Aspens

Mount Clarence King

Nevada Fall,
Rainbow

El Capitan,
Winter, Sunrise

Monolith, the
Face of Half
Dome

Pine Forest in Snow

Stream, Sea,
Clouds

Mount McKinley Range

# O R D E R    F O R M

**SHIP TO:**

Name _____

Address _____

City _____

State _____ Zip _____

Daytime telephone _____

*Please provide street address rather than post office box number as all shipments will be via United Parcel Service.*

| QUANTITY | | PRICE | AMOUNT |
|---|---|---|---|
| | **Books by Ansel Adams** | | |
| | The American Wilderness | | |
| _____ | Cloth (0-8212-1799-2) | $150.00 | $_____ |
| | Ansel Adams: An Autobiography | | |
| _____ | Cloth (0-8212-1596-5) | $65.00 | $_____ |
| _____ | Trade Paper (0-8212-2241-4) | $14.45 | $_____ |
| | Ansel Adams: Classic Images | | |
| _____ | Cloth (0-8212-1629-5) | $40.00 | $_____ |
| | Ansel Adams: Letters and Images | | |
| | 1916–1984 | | |
| _____ | Paper (0-8212-1788-7) | $29.45 | $_____ |
| | Ansel Adams: Our National Parks | | |
| _____ | Paper (0-8212-1910-3) | $19.45 | $_____ |
| | Ansel Adams: Yosemite | | |
| _____ | Paper (0-8212-2196-5) | $18.45 | $_____ |
| | Ansel Adams in Color | | |
| _____ | Cloth (0-8212-1980-4) | $60.00 | $_____ |
| | California | | |
| _____ | Cloth (0-8212-2369-0) | $50.00 | $_____ |
| | Examples: The Making of | | |
| | 40 Photographs | | |
| _____ | Cloth (0-8212-1551-5) | $45.00 | $_____ |
| _____ | Paper (0-8212-1750-x) | $34.00 | $_____ |
| | Photographs of the Southwest | | |
| _____ | Cloth (0-8212-0699-0) | $50.00 | $_____ |
| | The Portfolios of Ansel Adams | | |
| _____ | Cloth (0-8212-0723-7) | $40.00 | $_____ |
| | Yosemite and the High Sierra | | |
| _____ | Cloth (0-8212-2134-5) | $50.00 | $_____ |
| | This Is the American Earth | | |
| _____ | Cloth (0-8212-2182-5) | $50.00 | $_____ |

| QUANTITY | | PRICE | AMOUNT |
|---|---|---|---|
| | The Ansel Adams Guide: Basic Techniques of Photography, by John P. Schaefer, Book One: Revised Edition | | |
| _____ | Cloth (0-8212-2613-4) | $60.00 | $_____ |
| _____ | Paper (0-8212-2575-8) | $38.45 | $_____ |
| | An Ansel Adams Guide: Basic Techniques of Photography, Book Two | | |
| _____ | Cloth (0-8212-2095-0) | $60.00 | $_____ |
| _____ | Paper (0-8212-1956-1) | $38.45 | $_____ |
| | The Camera/Book 1 | | |
| _____ | Cloth (0-8212-1092-0) | $40.00 | $_____ |
| _____ | Paper (0-8212-2184-1) | $21.45 | $_____ |
| | The Negative/Book 2 | | |
| _____ | Paper (0-8212-2186-8) | $21.45 | $_____ |
| | The Print/Book 3 | | |
| _____ | Cloth (0-8212-1526-4) | $40.00 | $_____ |
| _____ | Paper (0-8212-2187-6) | $21.45 | $_____ |
| | **Posters by Ansel Adams** | | |
| | **Large format** | | |
| _____ | Aspens, Northern New Mexico (horizontal) (0-8212-2406-9) | $30.00 | $_____ |
| _____ | Aspens, Northern New Mexico (vertical) (0-8212-2428-X) | $30.00 | $_____ |
| _____ | Bridal Veil Fall (0-8212-2407-7) | $30.00 | $_____ |
| _____ | Canyon de Chelly National Monument (0-8212-2391-7) | $30.00 | $_____ |
| _____ | Cape Royal, Grand Canyon (0-8212-2409-3) | $30.00 | $_____ |
| _____ | Clearing Winter Storm (0-8212-2410-7) | $30.00 | $_____ |
| _____ | El Capitan, Winter, Sunrise (0-8212-2411-5) | $30.00 | $_____ |
| _____ | Maroon Bells, near Aspen, Colorado (0-8212-2185-X) | $30.00 | $_____ |
| _____ | Monolith, the Face of Half Dome (0-8212-2412-3) | $30.00 | $_____ |
| _____ | Moon and Half Dome (0-8212-2413-1) | $30.00 | $_____ |
| _____ | Moonrise, Hernandez, New Mexico (0-8212-2414-X) | $30.00 | $_____ |

*continued on overleaf*

Mount Clarence King
(0-8212-2610-X)          $30.00     $ _____

Mount McKinley and
Wonder Lake (0-8212-2415-8)   $30.00   $ _____

Mount McKinley Range, Clouds
(0-8212-2416-6)          $30.00     $ _____

Mount Williamson, Sierra Nevada
(0-8212-2417-4)          $30.00     $ _____

Nevada Fall, Rainbow
(0-8212-2390-9)          $30.00     $ _____

Oak Tree, Snowstorm
(0-8212-2419-0)          $30.00     $ _____

Oak Tree, Sunset City
(0-8212-2420-4)          $30.00     $ _____

Pine Forest in Snow
(0-8212-2421-2)          $30.00     $ _____

Redwoods (0-8212-2422-0)      $30.00     $ _____

Sand Dunes, Sunrise
(0-8212-2423-9)          $30.00     $ _____

Stream, Sea, Clouds
(0-8212-2424-7)          $30.00     $ _____

Tenaya Creek, Dogwood, Rain
(0-8212-2425-5)          $30.00     $ _____

The Tetons and the Snake River
(0-8212-2426-3)          $30.00     $ _____

Winter Sunrise (0-8212-2427-1)   $30.00     $ _____

Yosemite Valley, Winter
(0-8212-2183-3)          $30.00     $ _____

**Large format, color**

Late Evening, Monument Valley
(0-8212-2054-3)          $30.00     $ _____

Lone Pine Peak (0-8212-2055-1)   $30.00     $ _____

Yellowstone: Pool Detail
(0-8212-2110-8)          $30.00     $ _____

Yosemite Falls (0-8212-2107-8)   $30.00     $ _____

**Small format**

Rose and Driftwood
(0-8212-2030-6)          $20.00     $ _____

Thundercloud, Unicorn Peak
(0-8212-2029-2)          $20.00     $ _____

White House Ruin, Canyon de
Chelly (0-8212-2031-4)       $20.00     $ _____

**Calendars and Postcards by Ansel Adams**

Ansel Adams 2000 Wall Calendar
(0-8212-2577-4)          $17.95     $ _____

Ansel Adams 2000 Engagement
Calendar (0-8212-2576-6)      $17.95     $ _____

Ansel Adams Postcard Folio:
30 Photographs (0-8212-2105-1)  $10.95     $ _____

Ansel Adams Postcard Folio:
Winter Photographs
(0-8212-2135-3)          $10.95     $ _____

Ansel Adams Postcard Folio:
The National Parks
(0-8212-2181-7)          $9.95      $ _____

Ansel Adams Postcard Folio:
Color Photographs
(0-8212-2240-6)          $9.95      $ _____

Ansel Adams Postcard Folio:
Yosemite National Park
(0-8212-2283-X)          $9.95      $ _____

Ansel Adams Postcard Folio:
The Southwest  (0-8212-2344-5)  $9.95      $ _____

Ansel Adams Postcard Folio:
California Photographs
(0-8212-2478-6)          $10.95     $ _____

SUBTOTAL                      $ _____

California, Massachusetts, and New York
residents must include applicable sales tax.   $ _____

TOTAL                         $ _____

☐ I enclose check/money order payable to Little, Brown and Company
   for the total due above. Publisher pays postage and handling.
   OR

☐ Charge my   ☐ American Express   ☐ VISA   ☐ MasterCard
   $1.50 for one item, and $.50 for each additional item ordered, will
   be charged for handling. Postage will be determined by weight.
   Account number _____

   Expiration date _____ Signature _____

   Posters are non-returnable. *Prices shown on this order form are current
   prices and are subject to change without notice.*

**SEND ORDERS TO:**              **OR CALL TOLL-FREE:**
Little, Brown                    1-800-759-0190
Customer Service
Three Center Plaza
Boston, MA 02108                 Also available at bookstores